Thomas Jefferson

Thomas Jefferson

Academic Industries, Inc.
West Haven, Connecticut 06516

ISBN 0-88301-785-7

Published by
Academic Industries, Inc.
The Academic Building
Saw Mill Road
West Haven, Connecticut 06516

Printed in the United States of America

Thomas Jefferson

Contents

In seventeen days, young Thomas Jefferson put on paper a one-page document that changed the world. It was the Declaration of Independence. It told why the American people would fight England and King George to be free.

The Education of a Young Man

The earliest thing Tom Jefferson could remember was the day his family moved from one home to another.

Here you go, Tom! This will be a long ride for a two-year-old!

Before long, his father taught him to ride a horse by himself.

He also taught Tom to be friends with the Indians.

Chief Ontassete, this is my son Thomas!

Peter Jefferson was a surveyor as well as a farmer. Tom loved to hear about his father's trips into the wild country beyond Virginia.

Yes, there are mountains and swamps . . . and more wild animals than you can count.

I'd like to see the whole country someday.

When Tom was fourteen, his father died suddenly. Tom became the man of the family. He was helped by his teacher, the Reverend James Maury.

I am afraid I don't know enough to run a big plantation.

You will find that your father has taught you well. And his friends will help you.

Tom had little trouble running the plantation. And it made plenty of money for his family.

When Tom was seventeen, he talked with Reverend Maury about what he should do next.

Tom, I've taught you as much as I can. You have a fine mind. You should go to college.

Things are running smoothly. Your mother feels she can manage.

Then I'll do it! There is so much to learn.

At that time there were only three colleges in America. Tom went to the nearest one, William and Mary. It was several days' ride from his home.

I'd like that! And it's what my father wanted. But what about Shadwell, our plantation?

I'll reach the Dandridges' home tonight. I'm sure they'll welcome me.

15

William Small was pleased with his new student, too. He spoke of him to his close friends, George Wythe and Francis Fauquier.

He has a fine mind. He will become a great man!

Very well . . . bring him to dine with us!

Tom became friendly with all three men, sharing dinners and conversations.

Someday you must visit London and Paris.

Later, Tom would say that he learned a great deal that was important to him at Fauquier's dinner table.

Tom also played the violin with a music group.

He attended many dances.

And he went to plays.

But at the end of the year, Tom was not happy. He talked to his friend Dabney Carr.

I've wasted too much time and money. Next year, I'll study fifteen hours a day!

And so he did, getting up at dawn each morning.

Until eight o'clock I will study all about farming, science, and religion.

From eight to twelve he read law; from twelve to one he read politics; and in the afternoon, he studied history.

Come hunting with me, Tom!

Sorry, Dabney. I don't have time.

Every afternoon Tom ran to a place a mile beyond the town and back again.

From dawn until bedtime, he spent his time reading and studying. At the age of nineteen he was one of the smartest men in Virginia.

There he goes again!

When he finished college, Tom went home to Shadwell. He talked with Jane, his favorite sister.

What will you do next?

Become a lawyer, I guess.

Will you go to law school?

There aren't any law schools. I will work for a lawyer and read law books. Then one day I will know enough to become a lawyer myself.

Tom found work in the office of George Wythe, one of the best-known lawyers in Virginia.

You will read this and learn everything in it.

Yes, sir!

For five years, Tom studied hard. But he found time for fun, too. He danced, played his violin, and fell in love.

Rebecca is so wonderful! Maybe I'll even ask her to marry me!

I don't think Rebecca will wait for you. She is going to marry someone else!

In 1767, at the age of twenty-four, Tom finally became a lawyer. He also began building a house.

Here, on the highest point of my land, will stand a beautiful house. I will call it Monticello.

I will draw up the plans, build the house, and plant the gardens.

In 1770, a fire destroyed Shadwell.

Good luck!

The news was brought to Tom in Williamsburg.

Is the family safe?

Yes, sir. But everything else is lost—everything but your violin!

I won't build Shadwell again. I'll put my time and money into building Monticello instead.

20

Marriage
and Politics

That year, Tom fell in love with a beautiful young widow, Martha Wayles Skelton.

He told her of his plans for Monticello.

Only a one-room brick cottage is finished, but it will be a happy place.

On New Year's Day, 1772, they were married at Martha's home.

Soon after, Tom and Martha left for Monticello, two hundred miles away. Virginia was covered with three feet of snow.

I think we'll have to go on the horses the rest of the way.

That will be exciting!

The work began.

Another twenty feet this way.

Nearly everything needed to build the house was made on the place, even the bricks.

Good! These bricks are just what I want.

Soon the house was finished.

Babies were born.

A daughter! We will name her Martha!

As her family grew, Mrs. Jefferson became a busy housewife.

Thomas Jefferson continued his work as a lawyer. He was also elected to the government which met in Williamsburg and made many of Virginia's laws.

I really don't have time for politics. But because of our trouble with England, I must help in the government.

In Williamsburg Jefferson talked with friends.

With his new laws and taxes, King George is treating us like slaves instead of free men!

What are the other colonies doing about it?

We should write to them and find out.

I agree!

With their letters, these men helped to bring the colonies together in their fight against England.

In March, 1775, Jefferson listened to a speech by Patrick Henry.

Give me liberty or give me death!

News of his words spread to all the colonies. Soon after, American farmers fired on English soldiers in Massachusetts. The war for freedom had begun.

Working for the New Government

The leaders from each colony met in Philadelphia. Jefferson was among them. They chose George Washington to head the army.

In 1776, the Continental Congress met. Men were chosen to put America's problems on paper.

I vote for John Adams.

Benjamin Franklin!

Thomas Jefferson of Virginia!

The other men asked Jefferson to do the writing. He worked for seventeen days.

At last his words were read to the Congress.

". . . .that all men are created equal."

On July 4, the Declaration of Independence was accepted. People were very happy.

Tom went home in August. He said he would not serve again in the Congress. His wife was not well. He also had work to do in Virginia.

We must change the laws to make them fair.

It will take more than winning a war to build a country. Each person must be free to live as he chooses.

What do you think should be done?

For two years Jefferson worked on new laws. He was helped by George Wythe and George Mason.

This is a law that says a person can keep his land from being divided.

And this law states that all family property goes to the oldest son.

These laws allow large plantations that are owned by only a few men and are worked by slaves.

I want to see a country of *small* farms, owned and worked by free men!

Jefferson wrote new laws to end the ones he thought were not fair. They were passed by the Virginia government.

Much of his work was done at Monticello, where a son was born in May, 1777.

The boy lived only three weeks.

Meanwhile, James Madison worked with Jefferson on a law to keep religion free.

A man should answer only to God for what he believes— not to any government!

And there should be no government church!

Virginia accepted this law, too. Later, it would be a model law for the whole country.

In his spare time he did much building and planting.

Jefferson also drew up plans for freeing the slaves in Virginia, for free schools, and for doing away with the death penalty for most crimes.

Mr. Mazzai has sent me four orange trees from Italy.

In 1779, while the war went on, Jefferson was elected governor of Virginia. The state had no money and no way to defend itself.

Soldiers from England are headed for Richmond, our new capital!

We must move the government records!

He worked with other men until early morning. Then he moved his family away. Later, he returned to a spot across the river from the capital.

The British have taken Richmond and are burning it!

But the British left, and the next morning Jefferson was back at his desk.

If the British armies join, they will take over. We must move to Charlottesville.

The British general, Cornwallis, learned of this move.

Colonel Tarleton and his men must ride to Charlottesville secretly.

Tarleton's men can take Charlottesville, and capture Jefferson at Monticello.

Meanwhile, an American, Captain John Jouett, was spending the night at the Cuckoo Tavern.

British soldiers riding west!

He rushed for his horse.

I must try to warn Jefferson!

I have the fastest horse in Virginia! I must reach Jefferson before the British do!

For five hours Jouett rode over secret mountain paths.

Tree branches and vines cut his face and hands.

At 4:30 AM, awakened by the sound of horses, Jefferson rushed out.

Jack Jouett! What brings you here?

The British are just behind me! You must leave, sir!

Jefferson sent Jouett on to Charlottesville to warn the people there.

After an early break-fast, he sent his family away.

You'll be safe with our friends, and I'll join you soon.

Goodbye, Papa!

Carefully he burned some of his papers.

Then he mounted his horse and rode away. A few minutes later, the British arrived.

The Americans soon won a great victory over Cornwallis' army, and the war was over. Meanwhile, Jefferson's term as governor had just ended. At last he could go back to Monticello and to the life he wanted.

In 1782, the Marquis de Chastellux came to Monticello.

Beautiful! You are the first American to build such a beautiful and charming home.

The Marquis wrote about Jefferson:

"He is an artist."

But all summer Jefferson's wife, Martha, was ill.

On September 6, she died. For three weeks Jefferson walked sadly around his room.

When he came out, it was only to ride alone through the mountains.

His friends felt it would help if he were to get back into politics. He was sent to serve his state in the country's new government.

Tom, they need you there.

The country needs good laws . . . like those you drew up for Virginia!

He finally agreed and went to Maryland where Congress was meeting.

In six months Jefferson did more to shape the United States than most men can do in a lifetime. He worked out a simple plan for American money.

British money is hard to understand. But using tens, with dollars, dimes, and pennies, will be easy.

He got the states to give up their western lands.

Virginia gives up all her land beyond the Ohio River!

He helped the plan for forming new states.

New states should all be as important as the first thirteen. Only then will everything be equal.

The Northwest Ordinance of 1787, which did not allow slavery after 1800, was based on Jefferson's ideas.

In May, 1784, Congress made Jefferson a minister to France. He and his oldest daughter, Martha, sailed for Paris on July 5.

It's a beautiful new ship! The sunshine is wonderful, and the sea is as calm as a river!

Jefferson loved Paris. Above all he liked the books that he found there.

I must have this one!

You've sent several hundred home already!

But he was shocked by the government and the way the common people lived.

Most of your people are poor . . . and hungry.

We must have our own war to make things right!

Jefferson was still in France when that war began.

Later, he traveled through Europe, taking notes on everything.

Much time could be saved if we could travel by air!

The new Virginia capitol must look just like this!

He crossed the Alps to learn how rice was grown in Italy.

I must find out why this rice is better than our Carolina rice!

He found there was a death penalty for taking seed-rice out of Italy. But he filled his pockets anyway, brought some home, and helped to make American rice better.

It was December, 1789, before Jefferson and Martha went home to Monticello. His people were happy to see him.

No, no, my dear people, you must not! Put me down!

In February, 1790, Martha married young Thomas Randolph.

I am pleased!

A week later, Jefferson went north again to become Secretary of State in President Washington's new government.

You will have only five people working for you.

Washington's Treasury Secretary was Alexander Hamilton. He and Jefferson had different ideas about most things.

President
of the
United States

In 1797, John Adams was elected president and Jefferson, vice president. Jefferson was happy.

Hamilton is making it hard for Adams and me to run the country.

The time will come when you can change things!

In 1800, Jefferson defeated Adams and became president himself. He took office on March 4, 1801.

In two terms as president, Jefferson changed the country in many ways. One important thing he did was buy the Louisiana Territory from France.

Without a shot fired or a life lost, you have made the country twice as big! It will open the west to many people.

Now you, Meriwether Lewis, must lead a group out to explore this land!

In 1808, after forty years of public service, he went home to stay. He rode, he studied, he played with his grandchildren. He built things.

During his last six years he planned and managed the building of the University of Virginia.

Do you remember?

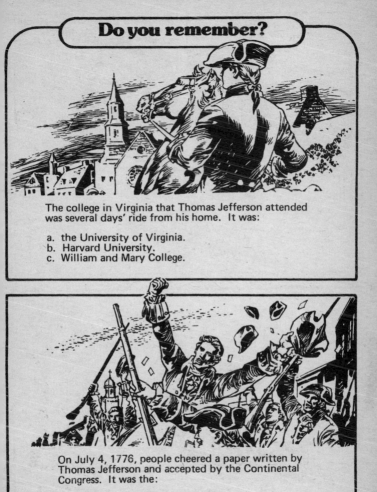

The college in Virginia that Thomas Jefferson attended was several days' ride from his home. It was:

a. the University of Virginia.
b. Harvard University.
c. William and Mary College.

On July 4, 1776, people cheered a paper written by Thomas Jefferson and accepted by the Continental Congress. It was the:

a. Gettysburg Address.
b. Declaration of Independence.
c. Constitution of the United States.

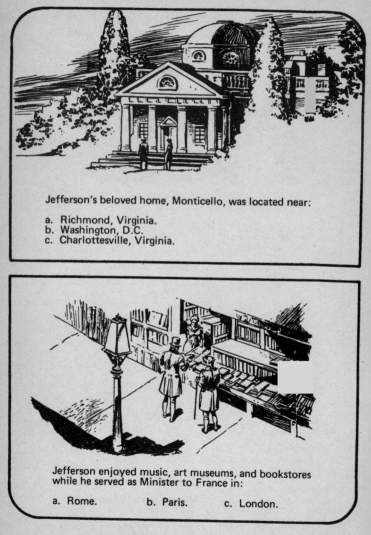

Jefferson's beloved home, Monticello, was located near:

a. Richmond, Virginia.
b. Washington, D.C.
c. Charlottesville, Virginia.

Jefferson enjoyed music, art museums, and bookstores while he served as Minister to France in:

a. Rome.   b. Paris.   c. London.

Quiz
Yourself

(Answers at end of section)

Words to know

document   an important paper used to record or prove something

colonies   area and people far from the country that governs them

congress   the law-making body of a government

liberty   freedom

territory   land belonging to a government, sometimes far away from home

Can you use them?

Using the words above, complete the following sentences.

1. Not wanting to give up their _____ , Americans have refused to be governed by any other country.

2. _____ passed many of the new laws written by Jefferson.

3. Before Hawaii became a state, it was a _____ of the United States.

4. The Declaration of Independence is a famous _____ written by Thomas Jefferson.

5. The _____ joined and fought against England for their freedom.

Using pictures

In reading illustrated stories, you will find it helpful to "read" the pictures as well as the words. Look at this picture. It shows Thomas Jefferson traveling to college. He had to go on horseback, over rough land and across rivers. Look at the other pictures in this story, and you will learn other facts about how difficult life was in early colonial days.

While you are reading

In addition to writing the Declaration of Independence, Thomas Jefferson did many things for America. While you are reading, make a list of the many ways in which Thomas Jefferson served his country.

_____

_____

_____

_____

_____

_____

How well did you read?

When you have finished reading, answer the following questions.

1. Why did Tom set up a strict schedule for himself after his first year of college?

   (Check the correct answer.)

   _____ a. He hadn't done well in his classes.

   _____ b. He really didn't like hunting with his friends anyway.

   _____ c. He felt that he had wasted too much time and money.

   _____ d. He wanted to become president one day.

2. The purpose of the Declaration of Independence was to tell the English king:

   (Check the correct answer.)

   _____ a. that he would have to pay higher taxes.

   _____ b. why the American people would fight to be free.

   _____ c. that the war was over and America had won.

   _____ d. that the colonies would fight with England against France.

POCKET BIOGRAPHIES

3. Which of the following laws did Thomas Jefferson want to see ended in Virginia because they were unfair?

   (Check the correct *answers.*)

   _____ a. A man owning a very large area could keep his land from being divided.

   _____ b. All family property went to the oldest son.

   _____ c. Slaves must work on large plantations.

   _____ d. Free men should own and work their own farms.

4. Congress accepted Jefferson's plan for American money because:

   (Check the correct answer.)

   _____ a. British money was too heavy to carry.

   _____ b. Jefferson gave the government millions of dollars.

   _____ c. they felt sorry for him because his wife had died.

   _____ d. using tens with dollars, dimes, and pennies was easy.

5. During Thomas Jefferson's terms as president:

    (Check the correct answer.)

    _____ a. he bought the Louisiana Territory which doubled the size of the United States.

    _____ b. America won the Revolutionary War.

    _____ c. he designed and built the University of Virginia.

    _____ d. he wrote the Declaration of Independence.

Using what you've read

Because Thomas Jefferson was an excellent thinker and writer, he was asked to write the American Declaration of Independence. One of the most famous statements in that document is ". . . that all men are created equal." The government of the United States is built on this one idea. Do you know what it means? In your own words, write a short paragraph telling what you believe the statement "all men are created equal" means.

THOMAS JEFFERSON

Can you use them?

1. liberty
2. Congress

3. territory
4. document

5. colonies

How well did you read?

1. c
2. b

3. a, b, c
4. d

5. a

NOTES

NOTES

NOTES

NOTES

COMPLETE LIST OF POCKET CLASSICS AVAILABLE

CLASSICS

C 1 Black Beauty
C 2 The Call of the Wild
C 3 Dr. Jekyll and Mr. Hyde
C 4 Dracula
C 5 Frankenstein
C 6 Huckleberry Finn
C 7 Moby Dick
C 8 The Red Badge of Courage
C 9 The Time Machine
C10 Tom Sawyer
C11 Treasure Island
C12 20,000 Leagues Under the Sea
C13 The Great Adventures of Sherlock Holmes
C14 Gulliver's Travels
C15 The Hunchback of Notre Dame
C16 The Invisible Man
C17 Journey to the Center of the Earth
C18 Kidnapped
C19 The Mysterious Island
C20 The Scarlet Letter
C21 The Story of My Life
C22 A Tale of Two Cities
C23 The Three Musketeers
C24 The War of the Worlds
C25 Around the World in Eighty Days
C26 Captains Courageous
C27 A Connecticut Yankee in King Arthur's Court
C28 The Hound of the Baskervilles
C29 The House of the Seven Gables
C30 Jane Eyre

COMPLETE LIST OF POCKET CLASSICS AVAILABLE
(cont'd)

SHAKESPEARE

BIOGRAPHIES

B 1 Charles Lindbergh
B 2 Amelia Earhart
B 3 Houdini
B 4 Walt Disney
B 5 Davy Crockett
B 6 Daniel Boone
B 7 Elvis Presley
B 8 The Beatles
B 9 Benjamin Franklin
B10 Martin Luther King, Jr.
B11 Abraham Lincoln
B12 Franklin D. Roosevelt
B13 George Washington
B14 Thomas Jefferson
B15 Madame Curie
B16 Albert Einstein
B17 Thomas Edison
B18 Alexander Graham Bell
B19 Vince Lombardi
B20 Pelé
B21 Babe Ruth
B22 Jackie Robinson
B23 Jim Thorpe
B24 Althea Gibson